What if mum wasn't human?

Story by Ruth E James

Character creation by Ellie A Roberts

Sometimes mum will say to me

"I'm only human dear!"

And that's what got me thinking,
What if this mum was to
disappear.......

What if my mum was a
dinosaur,
with **great big** teeth
and claws?!

My friends would line up in the street, to glimpse her as she **roars**!

But I guess she would be **stinky**, and not welcome in the park.

And with tiny eyes and **great big feet**, she'd be useless in the dark.

We would have to get a bigger car. In fact – can **dinosaurs** drive?

Without my weekly trip to **Grans**, I'm not sure I'd survive.

What if my mum was an **Alien**, and drove her own UFO?!

My friends could play up on the **moon**, until it was time to go.

But I guess she'd be no good at stories, unless she spoke English too.

And I'm not sure about hugs off an Alien, she might feel all slimy like **goo**!

We would have to paint her each morning, to stop her looking so **green**.

And maybe when you really think about it, that is a little bit **mean**.

What if my mum

was a **robot**,

with buttons that

beep and flash?!

My friends could bring their **robots** over, and we could have a big robot clash.

But I guess she would be no **fun** at all, when I want to splash in the bath.

And we could never go **exploring**, her wheels would need a smooth path.

We would have to keep her charged up, so she is always ready to **go**.

And when we play like heroes that **fly**, I'm afraid she might be too slow.

What if my mum was a

Dragon,

with wings that meant

she could **fly**?!

My friends could all take turns on her back,
and go way up in the **sky**.

But I guess she'd be no good at bedtime, when
kissing me goodnight.

And breathing out fire on the walk to school,
might give people a **fright**.

We would have to give up baking, no one likes a cake that is **burnt.**

And when playing **Knights** and **Dragons**, I'd need all the skills I have learnt.

What if my mum was a

Giant,

and boomed Fee-fi-fo-

fum?!

My friends could climb up on her back and slide down her ginormous **bum**!

But I guess she'd be no good at board games, the pieces would be too small.

Garden games would definitely be out, we don't have a **big** enough ball.

We would have to build a much **bigger** house, for her to come inside.

And my favourite game is hide and seek – How on earth would she manage to **hide**!?

What if my mum was a

Shark,

with five rows of glistening teeth?!

My friends could visit us under the **sea** and stare in disbelief.

But I guess she be no good at craft time, you can't hold a **pen** with a fin.

And maybe that's not the best choice for me, right now I can't even **swim**!

We would have to work out electrics, I can't leave the **TV** behind.

And I'm not sure how we could exercise the **dog** in a space that was so confined.

What if my mum stayed **only human,** would that really be so bad?

My friends already like her and she knows what to do when I'm sad.

She is great at **telling stories** and does all the voices **right.**

She loves to **splash** at bath time and knows that I like a kiss goodnight.

We wouldn't need to change her; we could simply **leave her be**.

I have discovered with all this thinking, my **mum** is perfectly designed for **me**!

A special dedication to all the mums out there, **perfectly** designed for your own little ones x

What if your mum was a dinosaur or maybe even a shark! Would you want to walk to school with her or take her to the park. Join one little boy as he imagines his mum as all these things and more before discovering his mum is just perfect for him.

@Ruthiesrhymes

ISBN 978-1-914408-02-1

John Tavener

LET'S BEGIN AGAIN

a singing tableau
for voices, instruments and children

libretto by
MOTHER THEKLA
taken from the Apocryphal Gospel of St John

CHESTER MUSIC

(a division of Music Sales Ltd)
8/9 Frith Street, London, W1V 5TZ
Exclusive distributor: Music Sales Ltd,
Newmarket Road, Bury St Edmunds, Suffolk, IP33 3YB

COMPOSER'S NOTE

Let's Begin Again is based on the story of the Dormition of the Mother of God, as recounted in the Apocryphal Gospel of St John. First we encounter Mary, praying at the tomb of Christ in Jerusalem. The Angel Gabriel appears and tells her that she will soon 'go to her Son'. Next we see Mary praying to her Son, this time in Bethlehem. She asks for the apostles to be sent to her. She tells St John that the Jews have sworn to burn her body. St John tells her that her body will not see corruption. The rest of the apostles 'fly in' from all corners of the world.

Many miracles of healing are now witnessed at the house, amidst scenes of general rejoicing in heaven and on earth. Back in Jerusalem, the Jews demand that the governor send soldiers to Bethlehem to seize Mary and the Apostles. As at the trial of Christ, the governor washes his hands of the affair, and the soldiers and people march on to Bethlehem to the house where they believe Mary to be. The Holy Spirit has warned Mary and the Apostles, and by a miracle they are transported to Jerusalem. The soldiers march into the house and find no one there. Instead there are flames of fire. Many are burned, as they cry "to Jerusalem! to Jerusalem!"

In Jerusalem Mary hears the voice of her Son calling her. She makes her final earthly prayer for the world. The Apostles take her body to Gethsemane. The funeral procession follows, and one by one the apostles bid her farewell. Finally, the body of Mary is raised to dwell in Paradise.

Because faith requires a constant 'beginning again', everyone joins in the last chorus of "Let's begin again", a quotation from Plato. The whole series of events seems to be starting once more but the music fades beyond our ears.

––––––––––––––––––

The story of the Falling Asleep of the Mother of God is retold here, using adult choir and instrumental group, and children who enact the story in highly stylised mime sequences.

The clothes of the children should be ikonographical, using strong primary colours. All the movements should be very precisely directed. It is suggested that the style of Ethiopian or Coptic ikons should be the model on which to base the visual aspects.   Naïve, in the best sense, and very direct.

Some form of flying apparatus may be needed to show the Apostles flying in from different parts of the world to be present at the 'falling asleep of the Mother of God', but other, simpler methods could be considered.

J.T.

This work was co-commissioned by the Norfolk and Norwich Festival, UK, the Greenwich Festival, UK, Musique Nouvelle en Liberté, France, and the Festival of Perth, Australia.

The first performance was given by the Britten Sinfonia, Choirs of Norwich Cathedral and Trinity College, Cambridge, conducted by Lionel Friend, directed by Lucy Bailey.

SCORING

Soloists (may be taken from the choir):

Mary	Soprano
Angel Gabriel	Tenor
Voice of God	Bass

Apostles:

John, Thomas, Matthew, Andrew Philip	Tenors
Bartholemew, Mark, Peter, Luke, Simon	Baritones
Paul, James, Thaddeus	Basses

6 Angels (semichorus or soloists (2 sopranos, countertenor, tenor, 2 basses*) singing from high up)

SATB chorus

*If the Angels are sung by soloists, the extra parts in the passage
 L1 to P1 should be taken by members of the chorus.

Orchestra:

4 recorders: 1. Descant doubling sopranino
2. Treble doubling descant
3. Tenor doubling descant
4. Bass doubling descant
Oboe
Clarinet in B flat
Trumpet
Trombone
Tuba
Timpani
Percussion (3 players):
tamtam, tubular bells, crotales, handbells,
large suspended cymbal, tabor, medium tomtom,
bass drum (muffled)
Harp
Piano
Organ (optional)
String quintet

Duration: c. 60 minutes
English vocal score on sale. Conductor's score, French vocal score and
orchestral parts on hire.

for Theodora

LET'S BEGIN AGAIN

John Tavener

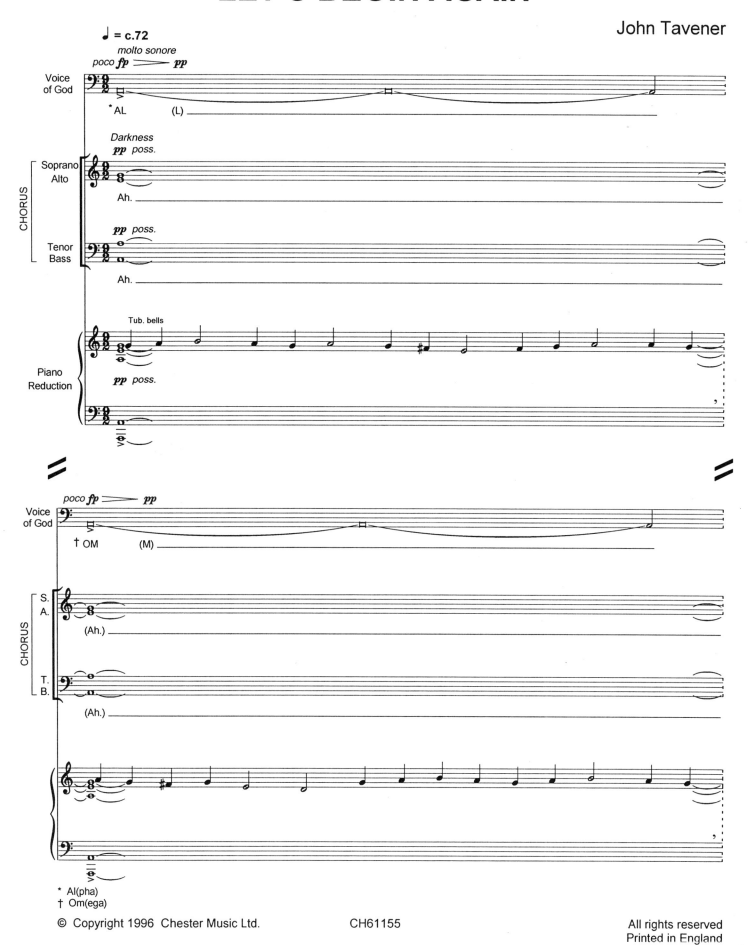

* Al(pha)
† Om(ega)

SCENE I

Jerusalem - the tomb of Christ

Light on stage. Mary is kneeling, with her arms stretched wide in prayer.

Very pure tone. Freely, as in Eastern chant - decorate with microtones ad lib.

* ♭, ♮ and ♯ denote microtones, the characteristic 'breaks in the voice' of Byzantine chant.

SCENE 2

Bethlehem. Mary is kneeling with her back to the audience.

P **Dance-like** (♩ = 100)

In Beth - le - hem _____ Ma - ry is pray _____ ing to Christ, her

son _____ and God,

THE ARRIVAL OF THE APOSTLES

16

John flies in - the first to begin the semicircle around Mary

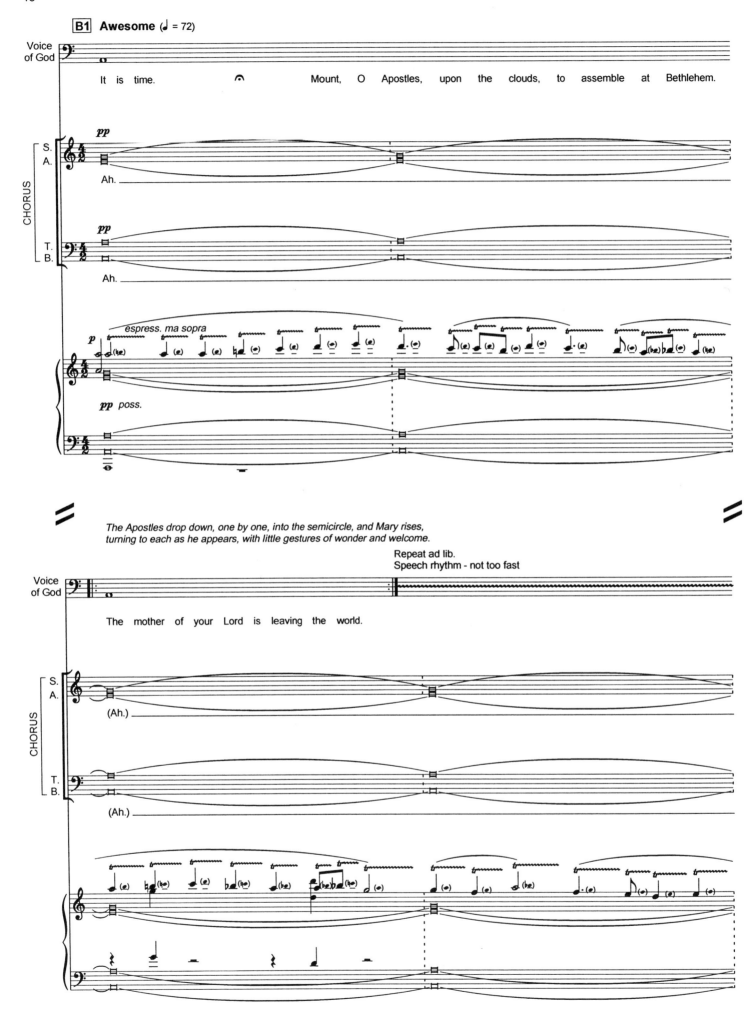

B1 **Awesome** (♩ = 72)

Voice of God: It is time. Mount, O Apostles, upon the clouds, to assemble at Bethlehem.

CHORUS
S. A.: Ah.
T. B.: Ah.

espress. ma sopra
pp poss.

The Apostles drop down, one by one, into the semicircle, and Mary rises,
turning to each as he appears, with little gestures of wonder and welcome.

Repeat ad lib.
Speech rhythm - not too fast

Voice of God: The mother of your Lord is leaving the world.

CHORUS
S. A.: (Ah.)
T. B.: (Ah.)

22

The mother of your Lord makes her departure.

Ah.

Ah.

G1 **Sonore**

From Je - ru - - - - sa - lem.

Awesome
like slowly tolling bells

Come.

Ah.

Ah.

Awesome

Voice of God: but not yet the Re- sur- rec- tion.

CHORUS (S. A.): (Ah.)

CHORUS (T. B.): (Ah.)

The Apostles come from the tombs.

Bartholemew (Bar.): From Thebes.

Andrew (Ten.): *f sonore molto* Ah.

Philip (Ten.): An- drew! Phi- lip! Luke!

Luke (Bar.): An- drew! Phi- lip! Luke!

Simon (Bar.): An- drew! Phi- lip! Luke!

Thaddeus (Bass): *f sonore molto* Ah.

Like a sudden lightning flash

sfp

* See Preface

M1 **Resplendent with joy and awe**

* 'Oh' as in the 'o' of 'log'.

32

SCENE 3
Bethlehem, Jerusalem

LAMENT I

Slightly slower

rit.

Lights up. A boy stands a little aloof. A gesturing group of priests shake their fists. They implore. They demand.
Finally the governor shrugs his shoulders. The people march on Bethlehem.

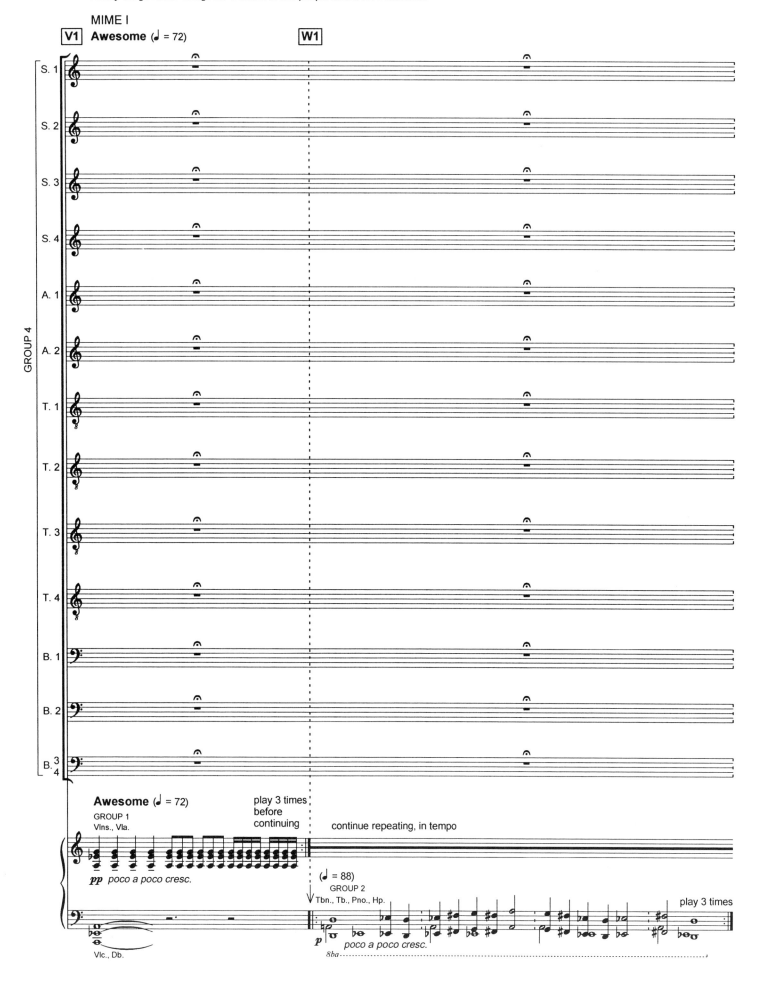

40

42

43

Highly stylised. Roman soldiers in some order. The people - a mob - pushing and shoving at invisible walls, throwing invisible stones, finally bursting open an invisible door . . . . . and then, UTTER BEWILDERMENT . . . . . FLAMES OF FIRE. They turn and rush off. Soldiers leave in a more orderly way.

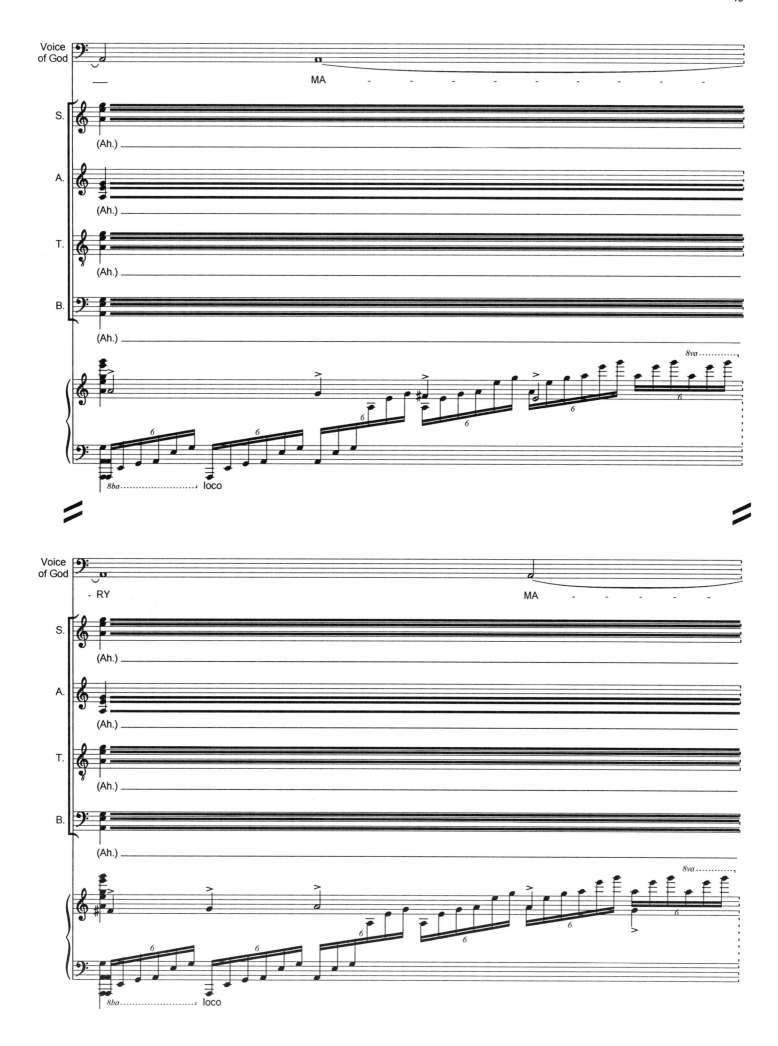

50

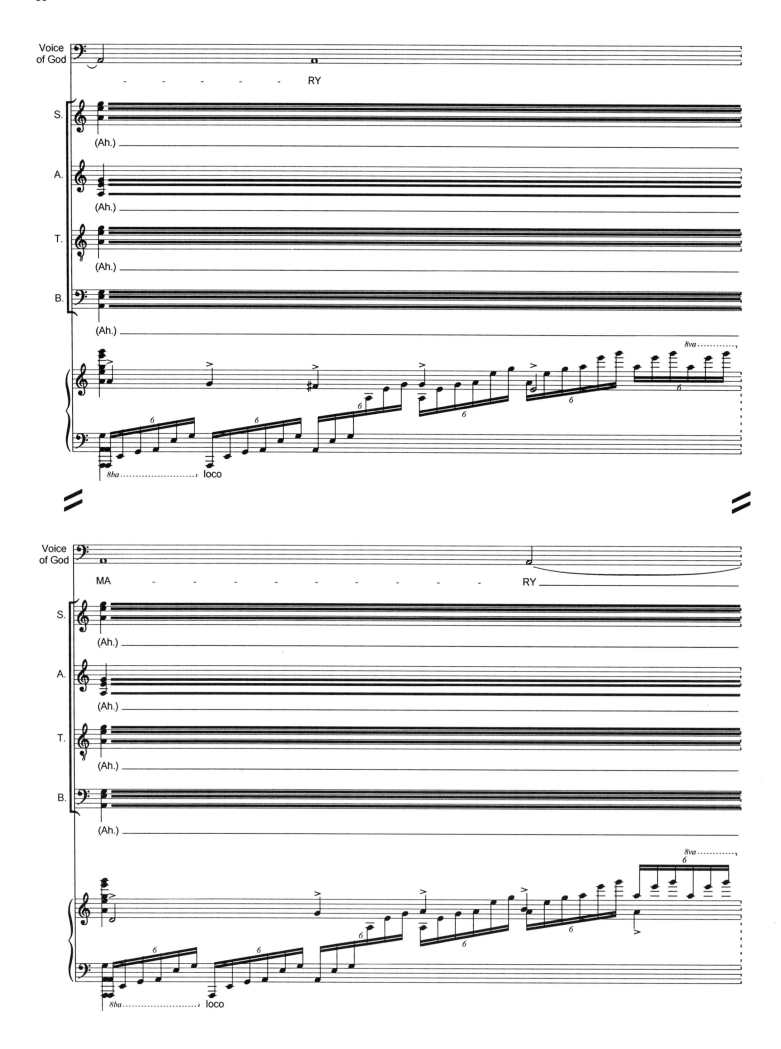

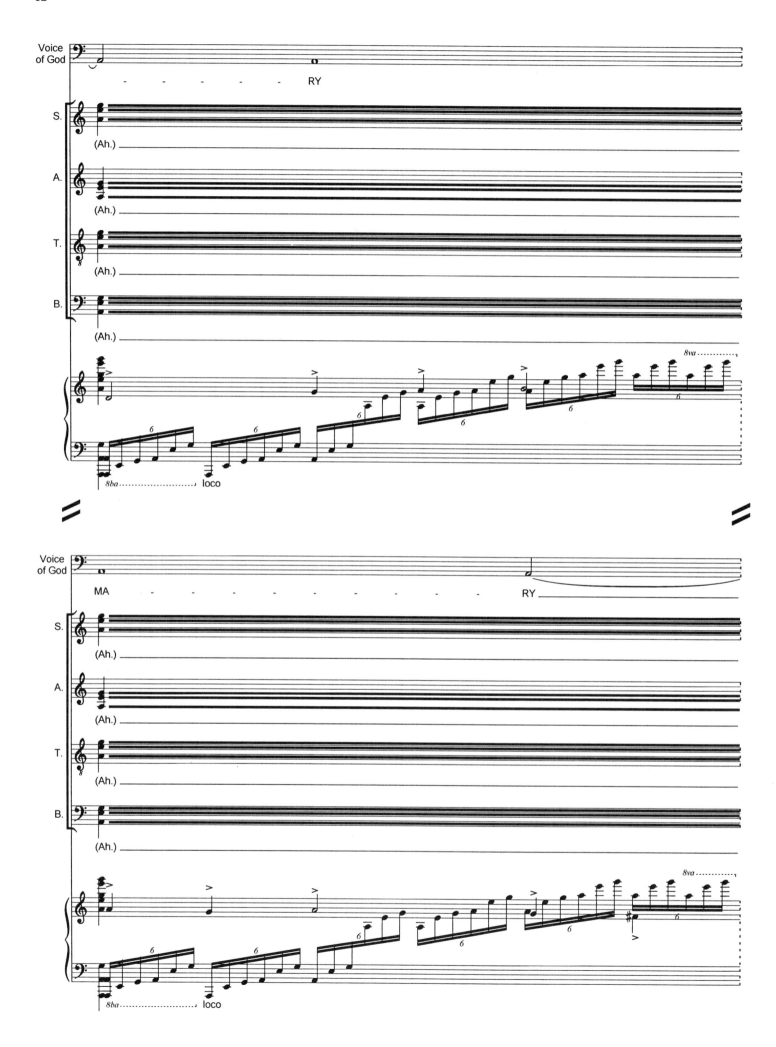

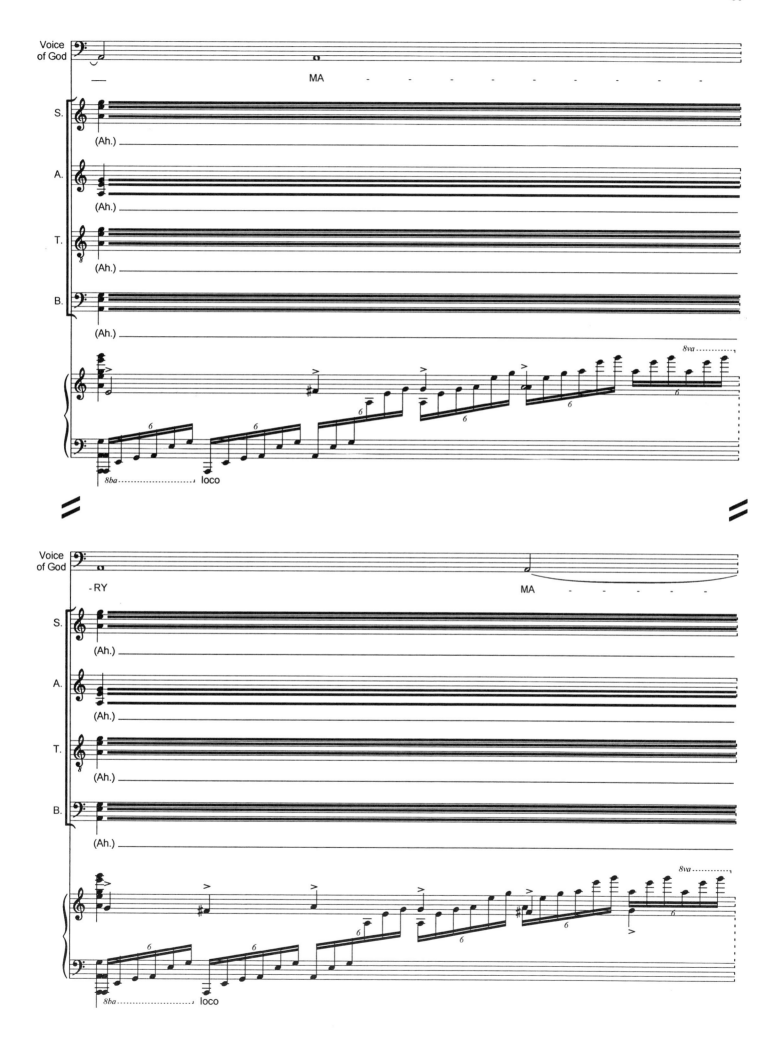

54

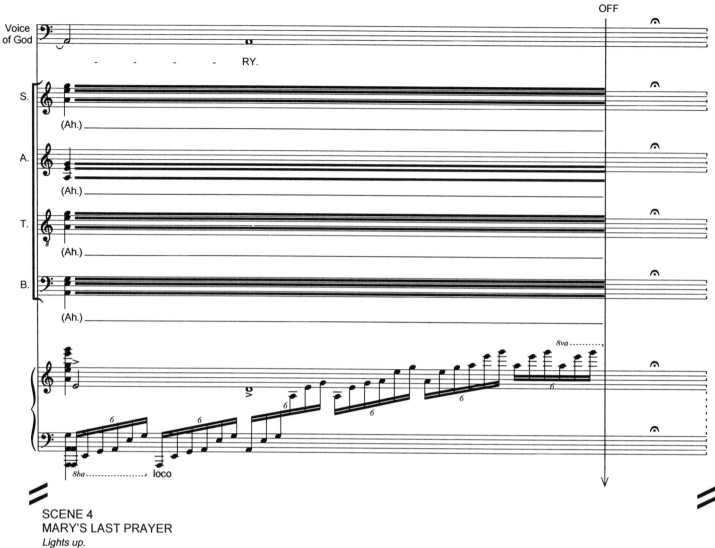

SCENE 4
MARY'S LAST PRAYER

Lights up.

Jerusalem. Mary and the Apostles are grouped together kneeling. Mary stretches out her arm to her son, as a mother to her child (Ikon of the Crucifixion). The Apostles bow down to the ground in fear (Ikon of Transfiguration).

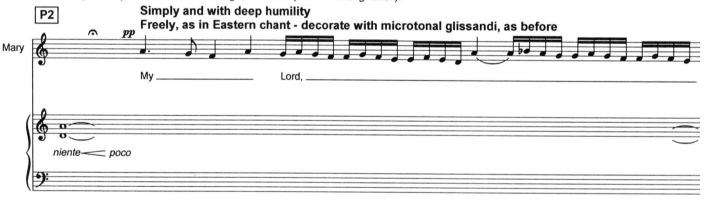

SCENE 5
Gethsemane - The Burial

FUNERAL PROCESSION

Lights up. The Apostles process with an open coffin in which Mary lies dead. People throng around. Then the winding procession starts.

Solemn - in the Byzantine manner (♩ = 56)

X2 **Sober - with Byzantine majesty**

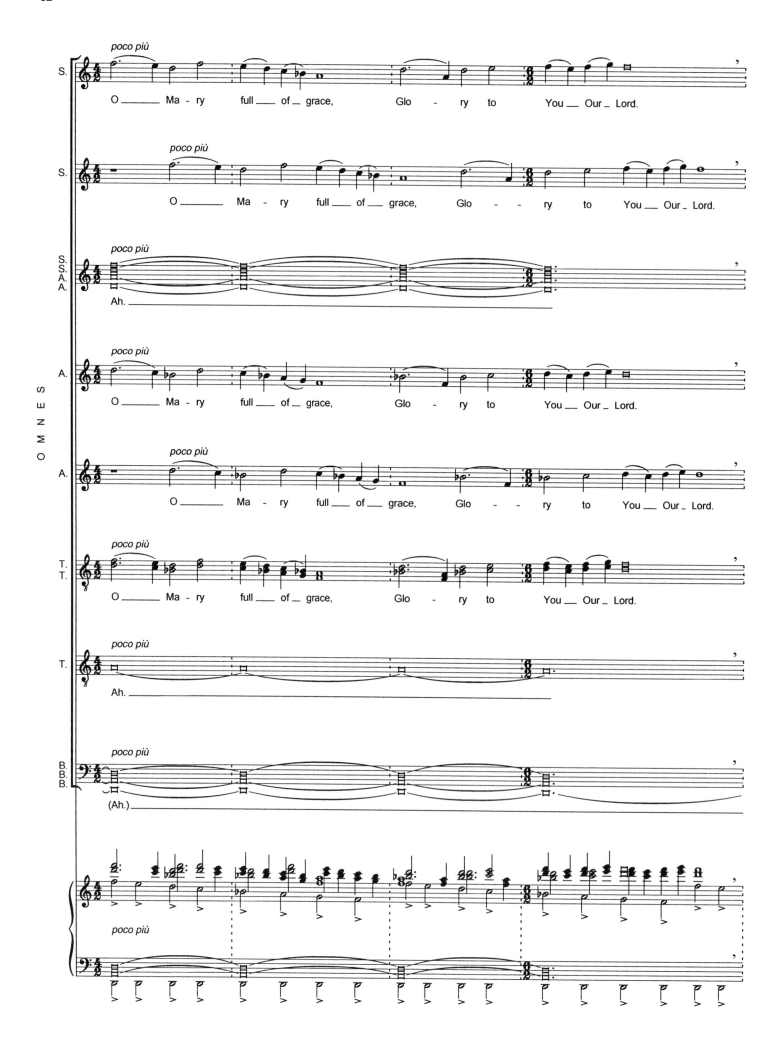

THE APOSTLES' FAREWELL

The Apostles gradually form the Ikon of the Dormition.

68

70

The body of Mary is raised to Heaven.

72

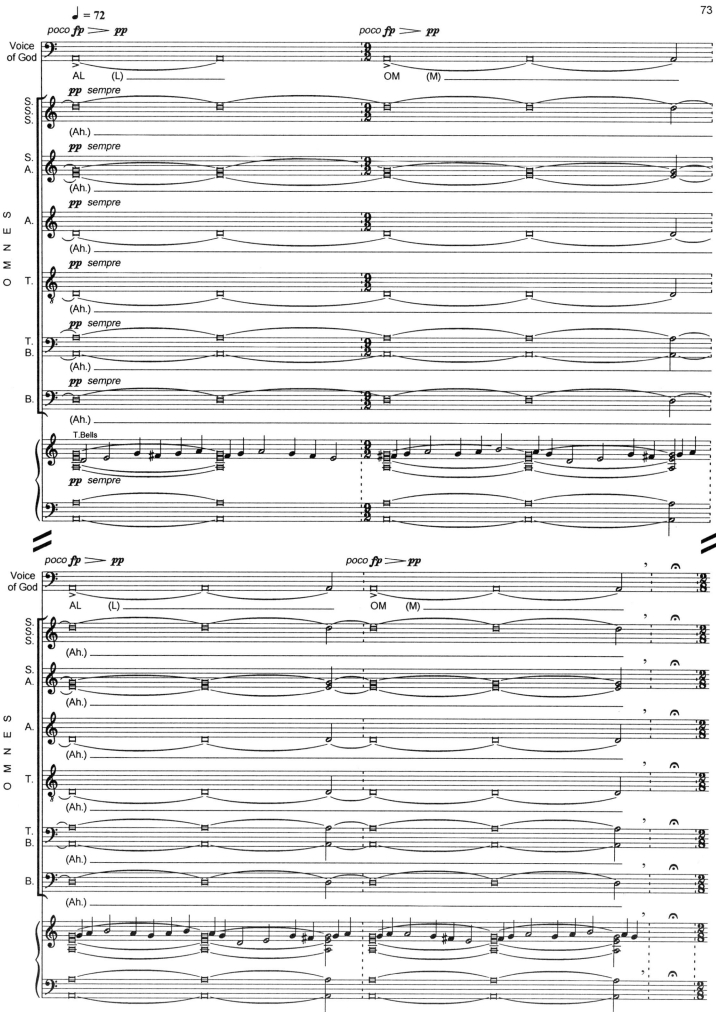

N'Aldretts
1992 - 1994